Here We Come

NEW EDITION

FAITH · AND · FREEDOM

Faith and Freedom

Nihil Obstat:

WILLIAM E. McMANUS, *Censor Deputatus*

Imprimatur:

✠ PATRICK A. O'BOYLE, *Archbishop of Washington*

WASHINGTON, JANUARY 25, 1951

COMMISSION THE

ON CATHOLIC

AMERICAN UNIVERSITY

CITIZENSHIP OF AMERICA

MOST REV. BRYAN J. McENTEGART
PRESIDENT OF THE COMMISSION

VERY REV. MSGR. THOMAS OWEN MARTIN, PH.D., S.T.D.
DIRECTOR

MARY SYNON, LL.D. **SISTER MARY JOAN, O.P.**
EDITORIAL CONSULTANT CURRICULUM CONSULTANT

PUBLISHED FOR THE CATHOLIC UNIVERSITY OF AMERICA PRESS
WASHINGTON, D. C.

NEW EDITION

Here We Come

By
SISTER M. MARGUERITE, S.N.D., M.A.

IN ACCORDANCE WITH THE EDUCATIONAL PLAN OF
RT. REV. MSGR. GEORGE JOHNSON, PH.D.
THE CATHOLIC UNIVERSITY OF AMERICA

Illustrations by Charlotte Ware

GINN AND COMPANY

BOSTON · NEW YORK · CHICAGO · ATLANTA · DALLAS
COLUMBUS · SAN FRANCISCO · TORONTO · LONDON

2

David

David, David.

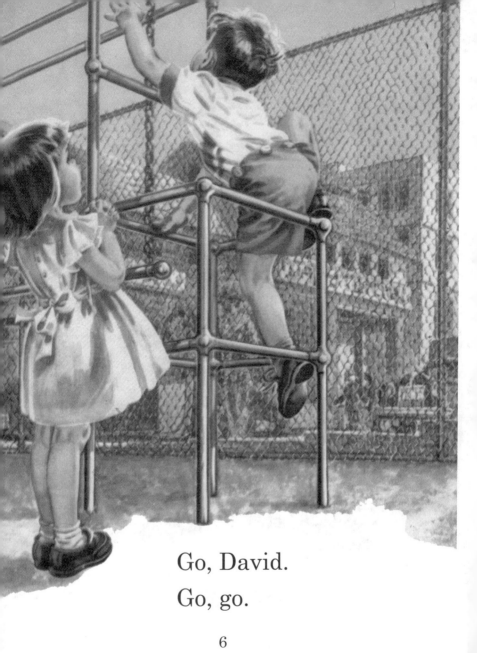

Go, David.
Go, go.

Go up, David.

Go up.

Go up, up, up.

7

Ann

Go up, Ann.
Go up, up, up.
Go, Ann, go.

Come, Ann.
Come, come.

See Ann.

See Ann come.

Come, Ann, come.

11

Mother

Come, Mother.
Come, see Ann.
Come, come.

See, Mother.
See Ann.
See Ann go up.

Go up, Ann.
Go up, up, up.

15

Come, Come

Come, David.
Come, Ann.
Come, come.

See, David.
See, Ann.
See, see, see.

Oh, oh.
See, see.
See, Ann.
See, David.

Father

Oh, Father.
Come, come.
Come, see.

Go up, Father.
Go up.
Go up.

See, Father.
See, see.
Oh, oh, oh.

Help Mother

Come, David.
Come, Ann.
Come, help Mother.

Go, David.
Help Mother.
Go, Ann.
Help Mother.

24

See David help.
See Ann help.

See David help Mother.
See Ann help Mother.

Help, Help

Oh, oh.
Help, help.

Come, Mother.
Come, David.
Come, help.
Help, help.

27

See, Mother.
See, David.
Oh, oh.
See, see, see.

Jesus

See Jesus.

Jesus can help.

Jesus can help David.

Jesus can help Ann.

Jesus can help Mother.

Jesus can help Father.

Oh, Jesus.
Help me.
Help Mother.
Help Father.

31

Find David

Father, help me.
Help me find David.

I can help.
I can find David.

Come, Ann.
I can help you.
I can help you find David.

Oh, Ann.

I can find David.

Oh, oh, Ann.

I can see David.

Can you see David?

Father Can Help

Come, Ann.
Come, see me.
Come, see me go.

Oh, oh, David.

Go, find Father.

Father can help me.

Father can help you.

See, Ann.

Father can help me.

I can go.

See me go.

Can you see me go, Ann?

Can You Find It?

Come, Ann.
Come, David.
Come, Mother.
Can you find it?

41

Can you find it, David?
Can you see it, Mother?
Can you see it, Ann?
Help me.
Help me find it.

Oh, oh.
I can see it.
I can find it.
See it, David.
See it, Mother.

Jesus Can Help

44

Come, David.
Help me.
Help me find Ann.
Can you find Ann?

45

Ann, oh, Ann.
Come, Ann.
Come, come.

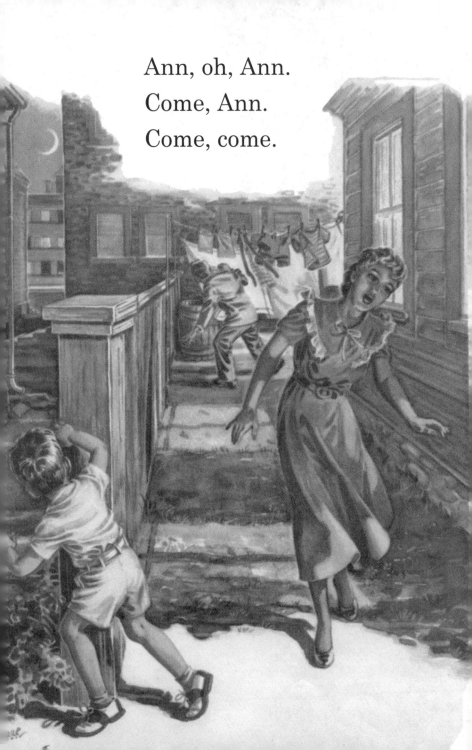

Oh, Jesus.

You can help.

Help me, Jesus.

Help me find Ann.

Find Ann, Jesus.

Oh, oh, oh.
I can see Ann.
Come, Ann, come.

Jesus can help David.
Jesus can help Ann.
Jesus can help you.
Jesus can help me.

48

To the Teacher

Here We Come, New Edition, is the first pre-primer of the FAITH AND FREEDOM Readers. It is followed by *This Is Our Home* and *Here We Are Again*. The 17 new words introduced in this first pre-primer are of basic significance and are repeated many times again in the other two pre-primers.

Here We Come initiates the program of Christian social living upon which the FAITH AND FREEDOM series is based. Mutual love and helpfulness in family life form the major theme of the content. Special emphasis is placed upon the virtues of love, respect, and helpfulness in the home.

Word List

2. _ _ _	14. _ _ _	26. _ _ _	38. _ _ _
3. _ _ _	15. _ _ _	27. _ _ _	39. _ _ _
4. David	16. _ _ _	28. _ _ _	40. it
5. _ _ _	17. _ _ _	29. Jesus	41. _ _ _
6. go	18. oh	30. can	42. _ _ _
7. up	19. Father	31. me	43. _ _ _
8. Ann	20. _ _ _	32. find	44. _ _ _
9. _ _ _	21. _ _ _	33. I	45. _ _ _
10. come	22. _ _ _	34. you	46. _ _ _
11. see	23. help	35. _ _ _	47. _ _ _
12. Mother	24. _ _ _	36. _ _ _	48. _ _ _
13. _ _ _	25. _ _ _	37. _ _ _	

This Is Our Home

NEW EDITION

FAITH · AND · FREEDOM

Faith and Freedom

Nibil Obstat:

WILLIAM E. McMANUS, *Censor Deputatus*

Imprimatur:

✝ PATRICK A. O'BOYLE, *Archbishop of Washington*

WASHINGTON, JANUARY 25, 1951

COMMISSION

ON

AMERICAN

CITIZENSHIP

THE

CATHOLIC

UNIVERSITY

OF AMERICA

MOST REV. BRYAN J. McENTEGART

PRESIDENT OF THE COMMISSION

REV. THOMAS OWEN MARTIN, PH.D., S.T.D.

DIRECTOR

MARY SYNON, LL.D.   **SISTER MARY JOAN, O.P.**

EDITORIAL CONSULTANT   CURRICULUM CONSULTANT

PUBLISHED FOR THE CATHOLIC UNIVERSITY OF AMERICA PRESS
WASHINGTON, D. C.

This Is Our Home

By

SISTER M. MARGUERITE, S.N.D., M.A.

IN ACCORDANCE WITH THE EDUCATIONAL PLAN OF

RT. REV. MSGR. GEORGE JOHNSON, PH.D.

THE CATHOLIC UNIVERSITY OF AMERICA

Illustrations by Charlotte Ware

GINN AND COMPANY

BOSTON · NEW YORK · CHICAGO · ATLANTA · DALLAS

COLUMBUS · SAN FRANCISCO · TORONTO · LONDON

See, See

See David.

See Ann.

See David.
See David go.
Go, go, David.

See Ann.

See Ann go.

Go, Ann, go.

Come, Come

Oh, Ann, come.

Come, Ann.

Come, see.

See it, Ann.
See it.
Oh, Ann, see it.

See, Ann.
See it go.
See it go up.

I see it, David.
I see it go up.

8

Oh, Help

Oh, Father, come.
Come, help.
Help it, Father.
Help it.

See, Father.
You can help.
You can help it.

You help David and me.
You can help it.

Help Mother

Oh, Ann, see Mother.
See Mother, David.
Mother helps you.
Mother helps you and me.

Run and help Mother, David.

Run and help Mother, Ann.

Run, run.

Run and help.

Blue, Blue

Oh, Mother.
I see it.
I see blue.
I see blue

14

Oh, Ann.

Can you see it?

It is blue.

Can you see blue?

15

Is it blue, Mother?
Is it for me?
Is it for David?

It is blue, Ann.
It can run.
It is for you.
It is for you and David.

It Can Run

See it, David.
Make it run.

Oh, it can run.
See, Ann.
It can run.

18

See it run, Mother.
I can make it run.
Ann can make it run.
You make it run, Mother.

A Blue House

See me, Ann.

I can make a house.

I can make a blue house.

See, Ann, a blue house.

I can make a house, David.
See me make a house.
I can make a red house.
Can you make a red house, David?

Oh, Ann.

A red house.

I can make a house.

I can make a blue house.

I can make it for you.

Can you make it red?

Can you make a red house, David?

Make a red house for me.

See, David.

A red house for you.

And a red house for me.

Blue and red,
Red and blue,
A red house, a red house,
A red house for you.

It is for you.

It is for you.

I can make a house.

I can make it blue.

Come and Play

Come and play, Mother.
Come and play, Father.
Oh, Ann.
Come and run.
Come and play.

See Mother and Father run.

See Mother and Father play.

See David play.

See Ann play.

Look for me, David.
Look for me, Ann.
Can you find me?
Look, look.
Can you find me, Mother?

Come, Mother.
Look, look.
Come, Ann, come.
Come and see.
I see Father.
I can find Father.

Work

See Father work.

Father works and works.

Father works for Mother.

Father works for Ann.

Father works for David.

Mother works and works.

Mother works for Ann.

Mother works for David.

Mother works for Father.

31

Ann works and works.

David works and works.

See David help Mother.

See Ann help Mother.

Come and Look

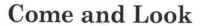

Come here, Mother.
Come here, David.
Come, come.
Come here, Ann.
Come and look.

Here I come, Father.

Here I come.

Here comes David.

Here comes Mother.

Look, Mother.

Here is a house.

It is for you.

It is for me.

It is for David.

It is for Ann.

Oh, oh.

Look, look.

See the house, David.

36

See the house, Ann.

A house for you.

A house for me.

Can You Come?

Can you come, Mother?

Can you come to see the house?

Come, David.

Come, Ann.

Come to see the house.

I will come, Father.
See, here I come.
Here comes David.
Here comes Ann.

Here We Go

Oh, we will go
To see the house,
To see the house,
To see the house.

Oh, we will go
To see the house,
Mother and Father,
David and Ann.

41

Here It Is

Oh, look, Mother.
See this house.
Here it is.
See this house, Mother.

Is this house for us, Father?

Will we work here?

Will we play here?

Will we work and play here?

43

This house is for us.
It is for you, Mother.
It is for Ann.
It is for David.
And it is for me.

Come, Mother.
We will go up.
We will go in.
We will go in to see this house.

Thank You

Thank you, Father.
Thank you for this house.
Thank you.
Thank you.

We will thank Jesus.
Jesus helped us.
Jesus helped me to find work.
We will thank Jesus.

In Jesus' House

Come, come.

We will go to see Jesus.

We will go in here.

We will thank Jesus.

Jesus helped me to find work.

See, Jesus is in here.

This is Jesus' house.

Look up here, David and Ann.

See Jesus' house.

Thank You, Jesus.

Thank You for the house.

Thank You for Father's work.

Thank You, Jesus.

Thank You.

You helped us, Jesus.
You helped Father.
You helped Mother.
You helped us.
Thank You, Jesus.

Jesus loves us.

Jesus loves us and helps us.

Jesus loves Ann.

Jesus loves David.

Jesus loves Mother and me.

David and Ann Help

Look, David.
See me.
See me help Mother.

Look, Ann.
See me help Mother.
See Father help.

We will work in here.
We will play in here.
Mother and I will play.
You and David will play.
We will work and play.

Look, David.

Look, Ann.

Mother will work in here.

We will help Mother.

We will help Mother in here.

You and I will help Mother.

See, Mother.
I will work here.
David can run and play here.
Ann can run and play here.
You and I will work and play.

58

Here Is Jesus

Come to me, Ann.
Come to me, David.
Come and see this.

See Jesus, Ann.
See Jesus, David.
This is for the house.

We will see Jesus up here.
Mother can work and see Jesus.
David can play and see Jesus.
Ann can play and see Jesus.
I can see Jesus.

Thank you, Father.
Thank you, Mother.
We love Jesus.
We love to see Jesus here.

Oh, Jesus
We love You.
We thank You.
Help us, Jesus.
Help David and Ann.
Help Mother and me.

To the Teacher

This Is Our Home, New Edition, is the second pre-primer of the FAITH AND FREEDOM Readers. It follows Pre-primer I, *Here We Come*, and precedes Pre-primer III, *Here We Are Again*. All of the words introduced in the first pre-primer are repeated in *This Is Our Home*. This second book may therefore be used as an initial text for the superior or above-average learners where the first pre-primer is not considered necessary. Of the 23 new words introduced in this pre-primer, one (starred in the list below) can be recognized independently by means of visual and auditory association.

Along with the acquisition of an increased foundational reading vocabulary, the pupil also acquires a further understanding of the first fundamental principle of Christian social living, namely, love. Through interesting story content, the child is led to see how God, the Source of love, manifests His Providence in the life of the individual through Christian parents and Christian home life. As in Pre-primer I, the virtues of love, respect, and co-operation in family relations are emphasized.

Word List

2. _ _ _	18. make	33. here	49. _ _ _
3. _ _ _	19. _ _ _	34. _ _ _	50. _ _ _
4. _ _ _	20. a	35. _ _ _	51. _ _ _
5. _ _ _	house	36. the	52. loves
6. _ _ _	21. red	37. _ _ _	53. _ _ _
7. _ _ _	22. _ _ _	38. to	54. _ _ _
8. _ _ _	23. _ _ _	39. will	55. _ _ _
9. _ _ _	24. _ _ _	40. we*	56. _ _ _
10. _ _ _	25. _ _ _	41. _ _ _	57. _ _ _
11. and	26. play	42. this	58. _ _ _
12. _ _ _	27. _ _ _	43. us	59. _ _ _
13. run	28. look	44. _ _ _	60. _ _ _
14. blue	29. _ _ _	45. in	61. _ _ _
15. is	30. work	46. thank	62. _ _ _
16. for	31. _ _ _	47. helped	63. _ _ _
17. _ _ _	32. _ _ _	48. _ _ _	

Review Words

2. see	6. come	9. help	12. Mother
David	7. it	Father	
3. Ann	oh	10. you	28. find
	8. up	can	
4. go	I	11. me	47. Jesus

PRINTED IN THE UNITED STATES OF AMERICA

Here We Are Again

NEW EDITION

FAITH · AND · FREEDOM

Faith and Freedom

Nihil Obstat:

WILLIAM E. McMANUS, *Censor Deputatus*

Imprimatur:

✠ PATRICK A. O'BOYLE, *Archbishop of Washington*

WASHINGTON, JANUARY 25, 1951

COMMISSION

ON

AMERICAN

CITIZENSHIP

THE

CATHOLIC

UNIVERSITY

OF AMERICA

MOST REV. BRYAN J. McENTEGART
PRESIDENT OF THE COMMISSION

VERY REV. MSGR. THOMAS OWEN MARTIN, PH.D., S.T.D.
DIRECTOR

MARY SYNON, LL.D.   **SISTER MARY JOAN, O.P.**
EDITORIAL CONSULTANT   CURRICULUM CONSULTANT

PUBLISHED FOR THE CATHOLIC UNIVERSITY OF AMERICA PRESS
WASHINGTON, D. C.

NEW   EDITION

Here We Are Again

By
SISTER M. MARGUERITE, S.N.D., M.A.

IN ACCORDANCE WITH THE EDUCATIONAL PLAN OF
RT. REV. MSGR. GEORGE JOHNSON, PH.D.
THE CATHOLIC UNIVERSITY OF AMERICA

Illustrations by Corinne Dillon

GINN AND COMPANY

BOSTON · NEW YORK · CHICAGO · ATLANTA · DALLAS
COLUMBUS · SAN FRANCISCO · TORONTO · LONDON

Up, Up, Up

Oh, Ann, look.
Can you see it, Ann?
It is red.
It is for us.

It can go up, Ann.
See, we can make it go.
It will go up, up, up.

You make it go, David.
Make it go up.
Run and make it go.

I can make this go, Ann.
I will make it go up, up, up.

Up you go.
Up you go.

See it go, Ann.
See it go up.

Up and Down

See it come down.
Here it comes.

Down, down, down.
We can make it go up.
We can make it come down.
It can go up and down.

David, I will make it go.
I will make it go up.
I will make it come down.

See it, David.
See it go up and up.
It will come down.

Oh, David, look.

It will not come down.

See it, David.

It can not come down.

I can go up, Ann.

I will go up for it.

No, no, David.

Find Father.

We will look for Father.

Father will help us.

Father can make it come down.

Down It Comes

Here is Father.
He will help us.
He will go up.

Look, Father.
It can not come down.
Can you help us, Father?
Can you go up?

Here it comes.

Down, down it comes.

See, here it is.

You can play.

Make it go up.

Make it come down.

11

Something in the House

Oh, Ann, run, run.

Run in to the house.

Run and see something.

It is something in the house.

It is something for you.

Will you come with me?
Come with me, David.
Come and see.

I will go with you, Ann.
You will see something.
It is something for you.

Surprise ! Surprise !

A surprise !

A surprise for you, Ann.

Look, look !

Oh, oh, oh.
This is a surprise.
This is fun.

It is fun for you.
It is fun for me.

See, Ann.

This is for you.

And here is something.

Look, Ann.

See this.

You can play with this, Ann.

David can play with this.

Oh, thank you.

Thank you.

Thank you for this.

Thank you for the surprise.

A surprise is fun.

Surprise Fun

Run and play.

You can have fun.

Here is something red.

You can have fun with it.

I will have a surprise for you.

Run and play.

Run and have fun.

This is fun.

It is fun to play.

It is fun to play with you.

This is fun for you.

This is fun for me.

Oh, look !
Look, look !
Here comes something.

It can run.
See it run.
Oh, here it comes.
Run, run, run.

Oh, look.

I see something.

This is David.

He wants to have fun.

He wants to make us run.

See, it is David.

Oh, this is fun.

Mother's Surprise

Come, come.

Come in to the house.

I have a surprise for you.

David helped me make it.

It is in here.

I want you to look for it.

You can find it.

Oh, here it is.
We see it.
We see the surprise.

Thank you, Mother.
Thank you for this surprise.

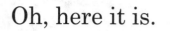

Mew-Mew

Oh, look, Mother.

Here is Mew-Mew.

Mew-Mew wants to play with us.

Come, Mew-Mew.

We will play with you.

We will have fun.

Look here, Mew-Mew.
We have something for you.
It is red.

Jump up, Mew-Mew.
Jump for this.
Can you jump?
Can you jump up here?

Here, Mew-Mew.

Jump up, up, up.

This is for you.

You can play with it.

Jump for it.

Mew-Mew is funny.

See Mew-Mew jump.

Funny, funny Mew-Mew.

No, no, no, Mew-Mew.

You may not have this.

You may not jump up here.

You may not play with this.

Jump down, Mew-Mew.

Jump down.

Oh, you funny Mew-Mew.

Come, come.

You may not play in this.

This is Father's.

Father will have a surprise.

He will see you.

Funny, funny Mew-Mew.

Fun in the House

Come, David and Ann.
We will have fun.
We will make something.
I will help Ann.
Father will help David.

Oh, this is fun.
It is fun for you.
It is fun for us.

Look, David.

See this.

See what we can make.

Mother and I can make this.

What can you make, David?

What can you make, Father?

Can you make this?

Look here, Ann.

Here is something I can make.

See what it is.

It is funny.

See what Father can make.

It is something funny.

Can you make something funny, Ann?

Oh, Mother, look here.
Look at Mew-Mew.

No, no, Mew-Mew.
You may not play here.
You may not have this.
This is not to play with.

Away with Mother

Come, David and Ann.

I want to go away.

You may come with me.

We will go away.

We will see something.

This is fun, Mother.

It is fun to go away.

It is fun to go away with you.

It is fun for me, Ann.

It is fun to go away with you.

It is fun to have you with me.

It is fun to have David with me.

Oh, look, Mother.
What is this?
It is big.
It can go up and down.
May we go up in it?
May we, Mother?

Come, we will go up.
We will go up, up, up.

A Big Surprise

See, David and Ann.
See what is here.
Look at the toys.
Here is a blue toy.
Here is a red toy.
See the big toys.
Look at this funny toy.

See this big toy, Mother.

May I have this?

I want it for Ann.

We can surprise Ann.

Ann can play with this.

It is big, David.

Find something little.

Ann can play with a little toy.

Oh, Mother, look at this.

See this funny little blue toy.

It can jump.

It can go up and down.

May I have it, Mother?

I want to surprise David.

David can play with it.

Find the Surprise

Oh, David.

We have a surprise for you.

It is a funny toy.

It is a little blue toy.

You may have it.

It is in this house.

Look for it, David.

Find the funny little blue toy.

Oh, here it is.

I see it.

What a surprise.

It is a funny little blue toy.

I can make it jump up.

Look, it can jump up and down.

Thank you, Mother.

Thank you, Ann.

Here, Ann.

I have something for you.

See what it is.

It is a surprise.

It is not something funny.

You can work with it.

And you can play with it.

41

Oh, this is not little.
This is a big toy.
I can help Mother with it.
I can help Mother work.

Thank you, Mother.
Thank you, David.
I will work with this toy.
I will have fun with it.

Jesus Is God

See, David and Ann.

This is Jesus.

Jesus is God.

God loves us.

God helps us.

God sees us.

God made us.
God made Father.
God made you.
And God made me.

God made this.

God made it for us.

Love God, David and Ann.

Love God and thank God.

45

David Makes Something

I want to make something.
Will you help me, Ann?
It will be big.
It will not be funny.
It will be for Jesus.
You will see what it is.

What will it be, David?
Will you make a little house?

Oh, no.
It will be a church.
It will be a little church.

I will help you work, David.
I will help you make a church.
We can play church.
It is fun to play church.
Come, David, I will help you.

Oh, Mother, come here.

Come here, Father.

See what we made.

Ann helped me.

See the little church.

See the little house for Jesus.

It is God's little house.

Is this God's house, Father?

No, Ann.
This is not God's house.
This is a play church.
God is in the big church.
The big church is God's house.

49

Here, David.

I have something for you.

It is something God made.

He made it for us.

See, David.

You may have this.

It is for the little church.

Fun at Play

Come, play with us.
We have something.
Ann helped me make it.
Come, see what it is.
See what we made.

What have you?

We can not see it.

Is it a little toy?

Is it something big?

We want to have fun.

We will play with you.

Here we come.

See, here it is.

See what David made.

I helped David.

We can have fun with it.

We want you to play with us.

It will be fun to play here.

Fun for you and fun for us.

Ann will be a mother.

I will be a father.

We will come here.

We will look at the toys.

We will play we want something.

Oh, oh, this will be fun.

What fun we will have.

Can you help me?
I want something.
I want it for Father.
Have you something for Father?

Is this what you want?
Father may want this.
See, it is little.
And it is red.

Here I come.

I want something big.

I want it for Mother.

Have you something for Mother?

Here is something.

It is big.

It will help Mother.

This will help Mother work.

What Is It?

Oh, David, come here.

I see something.

Can you see it, David?

What is it?

It can run.

It can jump.

What is it?

What can it be?

We will see, Ann.

Come with me.

We will look at it.

Come, run with me.

We will see what it is.

Oh, Ann, look, look.
What a surprise.
It is funny little Mew-Mew.

Oh, Mew-Mew.
What a funny surprise.
Come, we will help you.
This is not for you.
This is not to play in.
Go away, Mew-Mew.
Go away.

A Surprise for Jesus

Mother, may we go away?

May we go to the big church?

David and I want to see Jesus.

We have a surprise for Jesus.

I made it, Mother.

David helped me.

60

What have you, David?

What is the surprise?

May I see it?

Is this the surprise, Ann?

Is this for Jesus?

Oh, no, Mother.

This is not the surprise.

See, Mother.

Here it is.

Here is the surprise for Jesus.

Will you come with us, Mother?

We want to go to church.

We want Jesus to have this.

Jesus is God.

We love God.

Here, Jesus.
This is for You.
It is a surprise for You.
We made it for You, Jesus.
We want You to have it.
We love You, Jesus.

To the Teacher

Here We Are Again, New Edition, is the third and last pre-primer of FAITH AND FREEDOM. It is designed to provide the child with additional practice in reading vocabulary developed in *Here We Come* and in *This Is Our Home* before beginning the primer of the series. To achieve this purpose of greater mastery of a learned vocabulary, the words of the two preceding pre-primers are repeated many times in a simple and new context. Of the 24 new words introduced in *Here We Are Again*, five (starred in the list below) can be recognized independently by means of visual and auditory association. The gradual introduction of this new vocabulary enables the pupil to approach the primer with confidence in his ability to read.

The text features the same characters as in Pre-primers I and II. The pupil continues to follow the activities and experiences of David and Ann on a broader scale. The virtues of love, respect, generosity, and helpfulness are further developed in situations which the young reader can understand and appreciate.

Word List

2. _ _ _	17. _ _ _	33. away	49. _ _ _
3. _ _ _	18. have	34. _ _ _	50. _ _ _
4. _ _ _	19. _ _ _	35. big	51. _ _ _
5. _ _ _	20. _ _ _	36. toys	52. _ _ _
6. down	21. wants	37. little	53. _ _ _
7. _ _ _	22. _ _ _	38. _ _ _	54. _ _ _
8. not	23. _ _ _	39. _ _ _	55. _ _ _
9. no*	24. Mew-Mew	40. _ _ _	56. _ _ _
10. he*	25. jump	41. _ _ _	57. _ _ _
11. _ _ _	26. funny	42. _ _ _	58. _ _ _
12. something	27. may*	43. God	59. _ _ _
13.	28. _ _ _	44. made	60. _ _ _
14.	29. _ _ _	45. _ _ _	61. _ _ _
15.	30. what	46. be*	62. _ _ _
16. _ _ _	31. _ _ _	47. church	63. _ _ _
	32. at	48. _ _ _	

Review Words

3. for	4. and	5. this	12. in	17. thank
is	make	6. here	to	22. helped
look	run	11. play	house	29. work
red	we		the	36. blue
us	will		14. a	43. love

15